DOG PARK DAYS

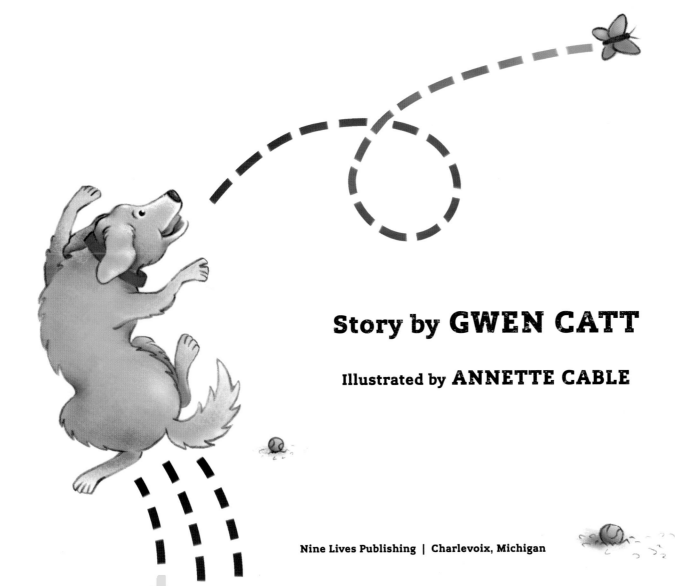

Story by **GWEN CATT**

Illustrated by **ANNETTE CABLE**

Nine Lives Publishing | Charlevoix, Michigan

To my family and friends, for believing in me.

Published by Nine Lives Publishing | Charlevoix, Michigan

Publisher's Cataloging-in-Publication Data
Catt, Gwen.

Dog park days / story by Gwen Catt ; illustrated by Annette Cable. – Charlevoix, MI : Nine Lives Pub., 2020.

p. ; cm.

Summary: Dogs enjoy and share a dog park in different ways; playing, socializing, and working through conflict, much like children on a playground.

ISBN13: 978-0-9601055-0-2

1. Dogs--Juvenile fiction. 2. Parks--Juvenile fiction. I. Title. II. Cable, Annette.

PZ10.3.C37 2020   2020914534
[E]--dc23

Project coordination by Jenkins Group, Inc.
www.BookPublishing.com

Printed in Korea by Pacom Korea, Inc., First Printing, September 2020, #35000-D7
24 23 22 21 20 • 5 4 3 2 1

All is still at the dog park.

The green grass, hiding an occasional hole, silently grows.

Trees await the continuous watering that is sure to come.
Sunlight gently peeks down on the peaceful park.

In homes across the neighborhood, young dogs, old dogs, and in-between dogs wake up and squirm in delight.

It's time to go to the dog park.

3

Toby arrives.

His long bushy tail sways
as he inspects every inch of the dog park
with his supersonic nose.

His nose knows.

4

Thanks to his hard-working sniffer,
Toby knows which dogs were here while he was away.

Toby can even sniff out the humans
that other dogs brought with them.

Toby makes his human "sit" during his inspection.

5

Jack barrels in on his drumstick-sized legs with his stubby tail held high.
He rushes immediately to the fence to watch the BIG dogs march past.
Jack just *knows* these other dogs fear him!

My human won't even get off the bench.

Bailey arrives, ignoring all the canines.
She has her human, Adam, to train.
He tries, but there's room for improvement on his frisbee throws.

Show off.

Bailey returns the frisbee to Adam's feet time and time again.
Training a human can be exhausting!

Together, two canine brothers, Kobe and Benson, arrive.
Eagerly, they sniff hello to old friends and new.

All over the dog park,
dogs run.

Dogs smell.

10

Dogs sing.

Dogs play.

Dogs rest.

11

Just like a playground at school, not everything is perfect at the dog park.

Kobe doesn't always like to share his water bowl.

Jack's barking can interrupt the chorus.

And Bailey is not pleased when a puppy tries to play catch with her frisbee.

But friends forgive.

Friends include.

Friends explain.

And, just like a playground, not everyone acts the same at the dog park.
Some dogs are eager to meet new friends, but some are shy.

Some dogs ignore the humans, but others love human attention.

Some dogs love to run, but others would rather wrestle and jump.
And, just like a playground, each and every dog has his or her very own look.

Not everyone enjoys the dog park in the same way.

Gus comes for the action. He is
crazy,
crazy,
crazy.

Addie comes for the relaxation. She is
lazy,
lazy,
lazy.

And that is simply "cool beans."

19

As time goes by, one by one, the dogs wander to the gate, telling their humans, "Come. It's time to go." Back at home, they have squirrels to chase,

mailmen to pester,

and naps to take.

Until the next...

22

dog park day.

Parents and Educators,

The primary purpose of this book is joy. The bond between readers and the children they read to is very special, and stories are often our fondest memories from childhood. In addition, children's literature is a treasured tool to teach with. In *Dog Park Days*, I use the following techniques to create joy and encourage children to author their own stories with care:

Strong Verbs: words that describe an action, state, or occurrence

Page 1:   await, peeks
Page 2:   squirm
Page 4:   arrives, sways
Page 5:   sniff
Page 6:   barrels, rushes
Page 8:   arrives
Page 14: forgive
Page 15: include, explain
Page 16: ignore
Page 20: wander, pester

Alliteration: the same letter or sound at the beginning of adjacent or closely connected words

Title: **D**og/**D**ay
Page 1:   **g**reen **g**rass, **p**eaceful **p**ark
Page 6:   **h**eld **h**igh
Page 7:   **b**arks **b**oldly

Repetition: the same word or phrase intentionally repeated

Page 2:   young *dogs*, old *dogs*, and in-between *dogs*
Page 9:   *time* and *time* again
Page 12: *Dogs* smell. *Dogs* run.
Page 13: *Dogs* sing. *Dogs* play. *Dogs* rest.
Pages 13 and 16: *Just like a playground*
Page 14: But *friends* forgive.
Page 15: *Friends* include. *Friends* explain.
Page 18: *crazy, crazy, crazy*
Page 19: *lazy, lazy, lazy*
Page 20: *one* by *one*

Font Changes:

      Page 6:   *BIG* dogs and Jack just *knows*

Personification: assigning human actions to a nonhuman

      Page 1:   green grass "hiding," trees "await," and sunlight "peeks"
      Page 5:   Toby makes his human "sit"
    Page 18:   dogs tell their humans to "come"

Adjectives: words that describe your noun

      Page 1:   *green* grass, *peaceful* park
      Page 2:   *young* dogs, *old* dogs, and *in-between* dogs
      Page 4:   *long, bushy* tail, *supersonic* nose
      Page 6:   *drumstick-sized* legs, *stubby* tail, *BIG* dogs
    Page 10:   *old* friends

All of these techniques can be taught to children. Below is a mini lesson on teaching young authors to use strong verbs. Note: like the students, the teacher writes during Writer's Workshop.

Writer's Workshop: Using Strong Verbs

Mini Lesson: Ask the students to notice what the author does. This is a technique called "noticings," as Katie Wood Ray has tagged it. The teacher then tries to mimic what the author does, and then the students try. Students are allowed to mimic the author's writing (or any mentor author's writing) as well as yours.

Introduction: Tell the students, "I noticed in *Dog Park Days* that the author uses action words more than boring words. Today, when I work in my writer's notebook, I will take the story I'm working on and use some of the words she did or some other words we know that will make readers say 'Wow!'"

Noticings: You might say, "I'm writing a personal narrative about fishing with my grandfather. I wrote, 'I woke up in the morning and was very happy.' In *Dog Park Days*, the author [page 2 from the book] tells readers it is morning and the dogs are happy by using exciting verbs and illustrations. Let's reread this page and notice how the author and illustrator show the dogs are happy."

Ask students to do the "noticing," but if they miss the word "squirm," lead them in that direction. Also point out the illustrations if needed.

You can encourage children to use more words by asking them to model what the illustrator does and then encouraging them to support their illustrations with words. Illustrations give students another opportunity to be successful and lead to countless teaching opportunities. Early elementary teachers might even consider teaching a short illustration study unit. Katie Wood Ray has a sensational book, *In Pictures and in Words*, to help teachers plan such a unit.

Suggest, "This page in the book would not have been as fun to read if it had said, 'The dogs got up in the morning and were happy,' so I'm going to try to use strong verbs like the *Dog Park Days* author used."

You might write, "In my bed, my eyes pop open, and I wiggle and giggle out of the covers." Point out the strong verbs "pop" and "wiggle" and "giggle."

Model multiple sentences on the board, possibly asking students to do this on their own as you proceed.

Give students a list of strong verbs such as the sample provided below. Support tools such as these give young writers confidence, especially those who will not use a word they can't spell.

Giving students a list of strong verbs also allows you to give a quick and powerful connected vocabulary lesson.

Movement Verbs:	Emotion Verbs:	Thought Verbs:	Senses Verbs:	Voice Verbs:
bend	frown	wonder	crunch	whisper
stretch	love	consider	lick	scream
bounce	grin	ponder	gobble	yawn
skip	cringe	question	devour	sob

Movement Verbs:	Emotion Verbs:	Thought Verbs:	Senses Verbs:	Voice Verbs:
skate	wince	agree	touch	sing
race/run	caress	daydream	savor	wail
dance	admire	ponder	pet	bellow
sneak	smirk	contemplate	feel	holler
skip	smile	plan	smell	cry
push	scowl	request	munch	snort
pull	grimace	demand	stroke	sigh
yank	stare	hesitate	rub	giggle
shiver	pout	quiz	eavesdrop	chant

I always leave additional spaces so students can add other words they find while reading or observing their fellow authors.

To help young authors create sentences that naturally allow them to use strong verbs, teach them how to begin their sentences with prepositions such as "in," "on," "under," "after," and "next."

Point out the sentence on page two of *Dog Park Days* that begins with the preposition "in": *In homes across the neighborhood, young dogs, old dogs, and in-between dogs wake up and squirm in delight.*

Tell students, "Just like in *Dog Park Days*, I intentionally used a prepositional phrase to start my sentence": *In my bed, my eyes pop open, and I wiggle and giggle out of the covers.*

Give students a list of common prepositions. With support and practice, they can learn to start sentences with prepositions. They won't all begin using prepositional phrases, but my approach was teach to the ones who would and expose those who might.

Next, model using prepositions to begin a sentence in a student's story. Perhaps a student explains that his story is about going to his grandma's house. He is happy to be going, and he is going in the afternoon. Ask students what we do around noon. In all likelihood, someone will mention that they eat lunch. Using this example, you could write, "After lunch, I dash to Mom's van, and off we go to Nana's house."

Be sure to write this sentence out; don't just verbalize it. Point out the preposition "After" and the strong verb "dash." Then ask, "Is this better than saying, "I am happy to be going to my grandma's this afternoon?'"

Facilitate a class discussion. Teach students how to begin sentences with prepositional phrases by making a list of times, such as *after lunch* and *before class*, and positions, such as *in the van* or *next to Mom*.

Repeat this lesson with a new example as many times as necessary depending on your class, their confidence as authors, and many other factors you will naturally recognize.

Now encourage students to begin playing with strong verbs in their writing. Honor your young authors' attempts, give them suggestions, and share their successes with the class. Building students up as writers gives them the confidence they need to try new ideas.

This lesson provides countless opportunities for future lessons and can be done in increments daily. You can select another strong verb from *Dog Park Days* and repeat the lesson using a fresh example but the same format to give young authors the repetition they need.

You can easily transition to adjectives by saying, "Let's describe the van that was taking our classmate to Nana's house." Or you can pick any other favorite opportunity from *Dog Park Days* or another piece of quality literature.

As a classroom teacher, I selected about a dozen mentor texts, knew them well, and used them for mini lessons virtually the entire school year. Most importantly, I created an environment for young authors to flourish.

Thank you for choosing *Dog Park Days* to further encourage and share the gift of reading and writing with children. Enjoy their journey and the bond this experience can bring.

Best Wishes,

Gwen

About the Author

Gwen Catt grew up in the small town of Kalkaska, Michigan. She started her teaching career when she was just a child, using a chalkboard and her brother and cousin as students. Later, she earned her bachelor's degree at Aquinas College and eventually a master's degree. After decades as a classroom teacher and literacy consultant, she retired and devoted her time to writing. Gwen splits her time between Charlevoix, Michigan, and Bonita Springs, Florida, the setting of *Dog Park Days*. She and her husband, Glen, have two grown children, Olivia and Tanner, and two dogs, Kobe and Benson.

About the Illustrator

Annette Cable grew up in the country outside of Columbus, Ohio, on a farm with her four younger brothers and lots of cows. She graduated from the Columbus College of Art and Design in advertising and illustration and now calls Louisville, Kentucky, her home. She has illustrated more than twenty children's picture books to date, designs and illustrates for several local historical museums, and teaches children's art classes. From her drawing board and computer screen, she creates book illustrations and wall murals and designs art classrooms and community centers. Regardless of the project, her teaching philosophy encompasses creativity, community, and education.